Dear Parent:

Disney's *Let's Discover Sea Creatures with Winnie the Pooh and Friends* is designed to be a fun and simple introduction to sea creatures for preschool-age children.

The activities also feature important early learning skills:

- visual discrimination
- fine motor skills
- patterning
- sorting
- counting
- early reading skills
- color, shape, and size recognition
- critical thinking

At the same time, Winnie the Pooh and friends will help your youngster discover all kinds of sea creatures! Your child will find that learning is fun and easy when done with these beloved Disney characters.

Welcome!

Come along and join Winnie the Pooh as Owl tells him all about sea creatures!

A sea creature is an animal that lives in or around the sea. Some sea creatures are mammals. Sea mammals cannot stay underwater all the time. They have to come up to the surface to breathe the air. Other sea creatures have shells, long arms, or sharp claws, and stay underwater most of the time.

A walrus is a sea mammal with big teeth.

A sea star is a sea creature with five arms.

A shark is a fish with a long nose.

So, what makes a sea creature a fish?
- All fish have fins.
- All fish have gills to help them breathe underwater all the time.

A clown fish is a brightly colored fish.

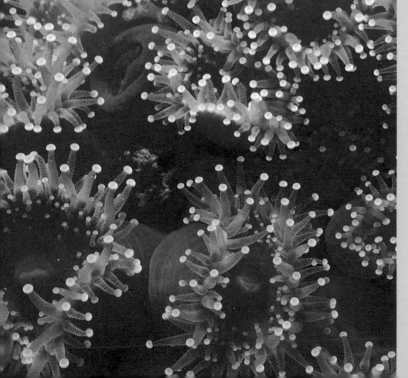

A sea anemone is a sea creature, too!

Sea Creature Patterns

Circle the sea creature that should come next in each row.

example

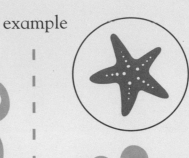

octopus   sea star   octopus

crab   seashell   crab

fish   dolphin   fish

Back to School

A group of fish is called a school. This young fish is trying to get back to its school. Complete the line along the path that will take it there.

Star of the Sea

A sea star is a sea creature with many legs. Can you count how many? Write the number in the box below.

_____ legs

Big, Bigger, Biggest

Sea creatures come in all different sizes.
Circle the biggest in each row.

hermit crab

dolphin

fish

Diving Dolphins

Dolphins love to dive! Trace the lines to help the dolphins dive.

Colorful Sea Creatures

Sea creatures come in many colors!
This fish has stripes, just like Tigger's!
Color the stripes on the fish below.

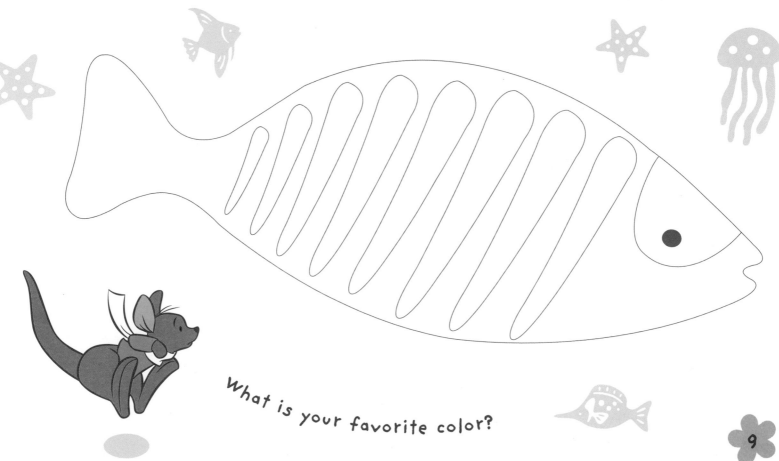

What is your favorite color?

9

Counting with Owl

Help Owl count the number of sea creatures in each picture. Write the number in the box under each picture.

_____ dolphins

_____ clown fish

_____ fish

_____ jellyfish

Find the Sea Creatures

Look at the animals below. Draw a circle around each one that lives in the sea.

butterfly

fish

sea star

sea horse

Do you like to swim in the sea?

ladybug

skunk

Pooh's Art Show

Help Pooh and his friends organize their sea creatures art show: take your sticker sheets and match the stickers to where they belong. That way, everybody can enjoy the show.

Octopus Colors

Some octopuses change color when they are happy, angry, or scared. Color each octopus on this page a different color.

a scared octopus

an angry octopus

a happy octopus

14

Safe Sea Anemones

Sea anemones help hide clown fish. Trace the lines to help the clown fish get back down to the sea anemones where they will be safe.

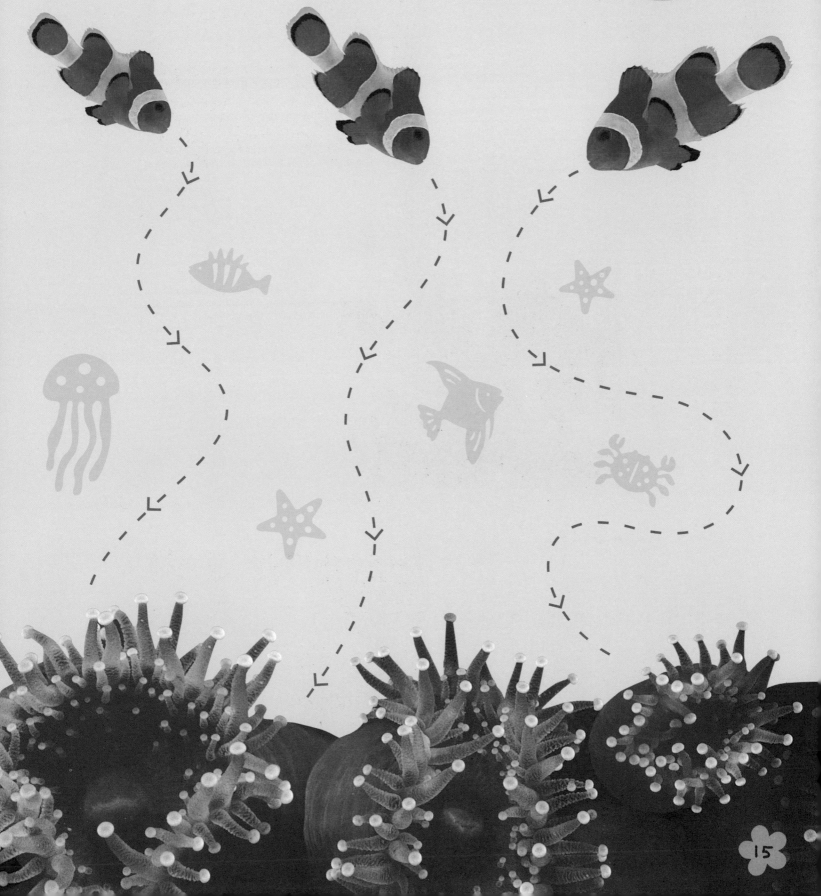

Owl's Creature Quiz

walrus

Walruses have big teeth called tusks. Can you think of another animal that has tusks?

- -

clown fish

Clown fish have colorful stripes. Can you think of an animal that has stripes?

- -

A daddy sea horse carries his babies in his pouch. Can you think of an animal that carries her baby in her pouch?

sea horse

Match the Sea Creatures

Piglet is looking for pairs. Draw a line to match the sea creatures.

whale

manatee

fish

turtle

turtle

whale

manatee

fish

Sea Creature Features

Find the sea creature that has a long nose.
Find the sea creature that has sharp claws.
Find the sea creature that looks like it is smiling.

dolphin

sea horse

lobster

My Favorite Sea Creature

Use this space to draw your favorite sea creature.
Write your name below the picture.

 My name _____

What's Next?

Help Eeyore color the sea creature at the end of each row to complete the pattern.

sea star

coral

seashell

dolphin

Rabbit's Mix-up

Circle the picture in each row that is facing a different way.

clown fish

shark

turtle

21

Answer key

page 4

page 6

A sea star has 5 legs.

page 7

page 10

4 dolphins **2** clown fish

 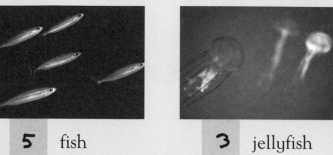

5 fish **3** jellyfish

page 11

page 16

Elephants also have tusks.

Tigers and zebras have stripes.

A kangaroo carries her baby in her pouch.

page 17

page 18

The sea horse has a long nose.

The lobster has sharp claws.

The dolphin looks like it is smiling.

page 10

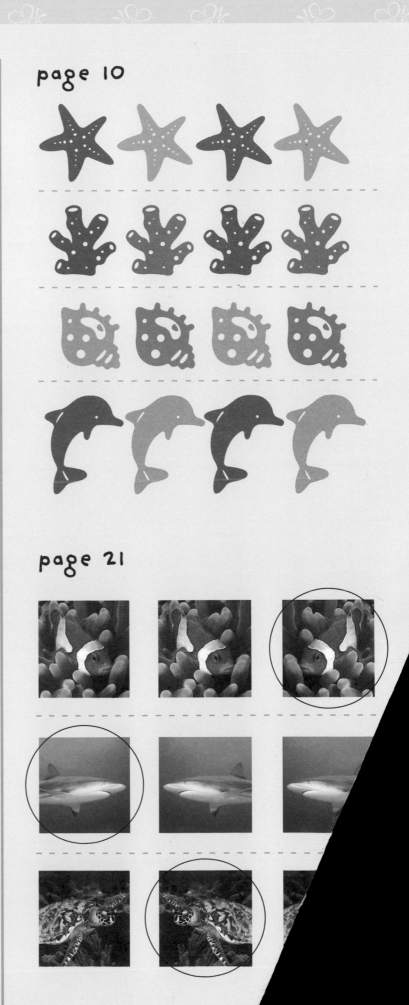

page 21

Written by Teresa Domnauer
Photo Credits:
Pages 7, 8, 18, and 22 Bios/Klein Hubert
Pages 2, 6, 11, and 22 Bios/Rotman
Page 7 and 22 Bios/Tavernier
Page 2 and 16 Sunset/Lacz
Thanks to Isabelle Southgate, Susan Ring, and Elsa Duval
Created by Editions Play Bac, Paris, France

For information address Disney Press,
114 Fifth Avenue, New York, New York 10011-5690.
Based on the "Winnie the Pooh"
works by A. A. Milne and E. H. Shepard
ISBN: 0-7868-5969-5
Visit www.disneybooks.com
of Congress Cataloging-in-Publication Data on file
First Edition
1 2 3 4 5 6 7 8 9 10

Printed in China